John Harrold

Rupert's Who's Who

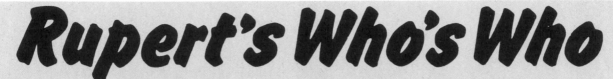

Rupert has so many friends and knows so many people that if this is your first Rupert Annual you may be a bit puzzled to begin with. So to help you, let's introduce some of the people you will meet or hear about, although one or two of them make only a very brief appearance in this book. Here they are —

BILL BADGER. A very close pal. Easy-going. Can take a joke. Useful in a tight spot. Always looks on the bright side. One of Rupert's oldest friends.

ALGY PUG. Another very close chum who has shared a great many of Rupert's most exciting adventures. At times just can't resist playing tricks.

BINGO. Very clever. Quite the inventor. Very curious and has to find out how things work. He is happy to go off on his own, but a good pal nevertheless.

PODGY PIG. Loves food. Doesn't like work. But even if he can be greedy and lazy sometimes, in the end he usually turns out to be good-hearted.

EDWARD TRUNK. Because he is so strong, a useful friend. Like most strong people he is really rather gentle. Always cheerful and ready to help.

WILLIE MOUSE. Rather timid. He'd love to be adventurous like the others. But he isn't. He does keep on trying, though. And that is really being brave.

PONG-PING. Comes from China. Very rich. Very proud. At times he can be quick-tempered but is kind and generous. Owns a small pet dragon.

ROLLO. The gipsy boy. A close friend of Rupert for a long time. Brave, quick-thinking. Lives with his wise old Grannie in a caravan and travels quite a lot.

The CHINESE CONJURER. More of a magician than just a conjurer. Lives in a pagoda near Nutwood. Has many times saved the day for Rupert and Co.

The SAGE OF UM. Clever, genial, but just a bit dithery. Travels all over the world in his Brella. Rupert first met him during an adventure with the Chinese Conjurer.

The WISE OLD GOAT. Very clever. Helpful, kind but mysterious. No one is sure how long he has lived in his castle in the hills which he seldom leaves.

The PROFESSOR. Rupert's old inventor friend, does not appear in this book. His SERVANT does appear. But no one knows much about him at all.

This Book Belongs To:

Katie Vicat.   Christmas 1984

RUPERT

CONTENTS

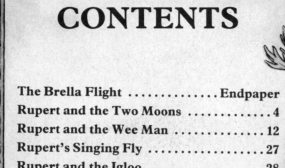

John Harrold

ISBN 0-85079-137-5

RUPERT and

See, Rupert stirs—it's past midnight,
Awakened by the bright moonlight.

Rupert stirs and opens his eyes. Something has wakened him. It is the bright moonlight streaming through his window. Sleepily he rises to pull the curtains. But a glance out of the window brings him wide awake. He stares. "Two moons!" he breathes. He rubs his eyes and looks again. Yes, there's the usual old moon, round and silvery. And there, a bit lower in the sky and glowing, is what looks like a second moon.

4

the Two Moons

He gasps. He stares in such surprise.
Two moons! He can't believe his eyes.

"Quick, let me find my telescope!"
Among his toys he starts to grope.

"Quick! My telescope!" Rupert scrambles over
to his toy cupboard. But by the time he has
found the telescope and returned to the window
the second "moon" has disappeared. In vain he
sweeps the night sky with his telescope. There is
no trace of the strange thing. Very puzzled he
puts away the telescope and gets back into bed.
"I know," he thinks. "Tomorrow I shall ask the
Chinese Conjurer. He knows about stars."

Alas, it's gone. What now? "I know!
To ask the Conjurer I'll go."

John Harrold.

5

RUPERT'S FRIENDS DISAGREE

Bingo has seen it too and thought
The Conjurer would know what's what.

He quietly hears what they've to say
Then tells the chums, "Do come this way."

The Wise Old Goat is there. What's more,
There's someone Rupert met before.

"The Goat can't change the Sage's mind.
That 'moon' you saw he's vowed to find."

Next morning Rupert sets out for the home of his clever friend the Chinese Conjurer. He is almost there when who should he see but his chum Bingo. "Hello!" calls the pup. "I'm on my way to ask the Conjurer about . . ." ". . . that moon thing that appeared last night!" Rupert breaks in. "Then you saw it too!" cries Bingo. "Come on, let's both go and ask!" The Conjurer greets them at the front door and listens quietly to what they have to say. Then, "Come this way," he says and leads the chums to his study. Two people Rupert knows are already there; the Wise Old Goat who seldom leaves his castle in the hills, and the genial Sage of Um whom he met on an earlier adventure with the Conjurer. Rupert notices that the Goat, usually gentle and friendly, looks grave. "The Sage," explains the Conjurer, "has also seen the thing you saw in the sky and is determined to find it. My other friend, the Wise Old Goat, strongly believes he should not even try."

RUPERT TRIES TO STOP A TRIP

Astonished, Rupert hears his chum
Tell the Sage that he'd like to come.

"Yes, come," the man says, "I don't mind."
And leaves with Bingo close behind.

The Sage's Brella starts to rise.
"Oh, stop! Please do stop!" Rupert cries.

Believing Rupert's changed his mind,
The others think they're being kind.

"He won't tell me why I shouldn't go," says the Sage. "So I'm going!" The Wise Old Goat shakes his head. He rises and addresses the Conjurer: "I must return to my home." He bows and stalks out. The Sage isn't at all upset. "He means well," he grins. "But I am going and I'm going now. My Brella's waiting outside." He bounces up and starts to leave. "Oh, I wish I could go too!" bursts out Bingo who can't resist any sort of exploring. "Come along then!" laughs the Sage and sweeps out. "Coming Rupert?" Bingo calls as he hurries after him. "We must stop them!" the Conjurer cries. "I'm sure the Goat knows something about this 'moon'." "I'll try!" Rupert says and races after Bingo. He finds him settling into the Brella, the Sage's strange craft. The Sage and he are laughing and excited. "Oh, stop, stop!" Rupert shouts as the Brella starts to rise. "Ah, so you've decided to come!" cries Bingo. And to Rupert's horror they haul him aboard!

RUPERT REACHES THE 'MOON'

"We can't go back. It's much too soon."
The Sage says, then, "Oh, look! Our 'moon'!"

The Brella heads towards the sphere
Which darts away as they get near.

The sphere seems to give up the chase.
Now, still and quiet, it keeps its place.

Then silently a door yawns wide.
Our fearful three are drawn inside.

The Sage and Bingo are so excited they don't understand what Rupert was trying to do. And by the time he has his breath back and can tell them they are high above the clouds. "Oh, dear!" says the Sage, "we've come too far to turn back now ... anyway, look!" He points and there in the sky is the strange sphere. "Hold tight!" he cries. He turns the Brella's handle towards the sphere, twiddles a ring on the handle and the Brella races towards the mysterious object.

To the three's astonishment the sphere zips off in the opposite direction then stops. The Sage turns the Brella towards it. The same thing happens. He tries again. But this time the sphere waits. The chums' eyes widen and they hold their breath as the sphere gets nearer and nearer until it seems to fill the sky ahead. Then ... "Oh, no!" Rupert gasps. A door in the sphere has slid open. Desperately the Sage tries to turn the Brella. In vain! They are drawn into the sphere.

RUPERT GETS A SHOCK

*A solemn voice asks, "Why do you
Our sphere across the sky pursue?"*

*"Our friend, the Wise Old Goat!" they cry.
The figure answers, "No, not I."*

*From all the doors around the sphere
Many more Wise Old Goats appear.*

*With sinking hearts our three now learn
They must stay here. They can't return.*

The Brella comes to rest inside a great domed chamber. The light from above is a gentle blue. A solemn voice demands, "Why do you pursue us?" No one is to be seen. "Show yourself," quavers the Sage. A silent pause. Then one of the doors on a gallery overhead opens and out steps ... "Our Wise Old Goat!" Rupert and Bingo gasp. The figure above speaks: "Not *your* Wise Old Goat. Just *a* Wise Old Goat. One of many." At that, all the doors onto the gallery open and from each steps another Wise Old Goat. They look stern. Our three gasp. They are quite bewildered. And frightened. "Oh, please, we meant no harm!" Rupert cries. "We want to go home!" pleads Bingo. "Yes, we'll, er, just be getting back now," ventures the Sage. Almost as one, the figures on the gallery lean forward and grasp the handrail. The one who first appeared speaks: "I regret that we cannot allow you to do that." The others chorus, "Oh dear, no! Quite out of the question!"

RUPERT'S FRIEND TURNS UP

"For peace and quiet we chose this sphere.
No one on Earth must know we're here."

They summon Nutwood's Goat to see
If he can somehow help our three.

Far too amazed to speak, they stare.
The Wise Old Goat they know stands there.

Thinks Rupert, "That's a funny thing,
That big History Clock to bring."

"You see," says the first Goat quite kindly, "we decided to live in this sphere because we need peace and quiet to study and think. No one on Earth must know we are here except your Wise Old Goat who stayed behind to keep us in touch with Earth . . ." "Oh, if only he were here," Rupert breaks in, "he'd tell you we wouldn't give away your secret." "You would not mean to . . ." smiles the Goat. "But at least let us summon him. He may have something to say that would help." He turns to the others: "Let us summon our brother from Nutwood!" The Goats shut their eyes as if they are thinking very hard. Gradually their horns start to glow. When the glow is brightest the Wise Old Goat from Nutwood just appears beside Rupert and the others. With him he has what looks like a grandfather clock. With a start Rupert recognises it. "The History Clock!" he whispers and remembers how once he tampered with it and was carried back hundreds of years. What is it doing here?

RUPERT FORGETS IT ALL

*"I'll take them back in time and then
They'll never think of this again."*

*The History Clock spins and, Lo!
Now racing back through time they go.*

*All that the three have heard and seen,
When they awake, just won't have been.*

*This time there is no cause to stare.
There's only one moon shining there.*

The thought waves that brought the Wise Old Goat must also have told him what has happened for he asks no questions. The Sage breaks the silence: "Goat, I am sorry. I should have known you had a good reason for not wanting us to seek this sphere. If only it was possible to go back to before we ever saw it . . ." The Wise Old Goat gives a small smile and says, "If my brother Goats agree we shall do just that." He looks enquiringly at them. "Agreed!" they chorus and at that moment Rupert turns to the bewildered Sage and Bingo. "Of course!" he gasps. "The History Clock! It took me back in time once before. He must mean to . . ." But the hands are already spinning backwards. Rupert hears his own voice echo and fade. He seems to be floating, nicely drowsy, dri-i-fting . . .

Rupert stirs in his bed. The bright moonlight has wakened him. Sleepily he rises to close the curtains. He looks out at the night sky over Nutwood. Nice, normal Nutwood. Back to bed.

RUPERT

Long before breakfast every day
The milkman comes round Rupert's way.

The jangle of milk churns wakens Rupert. He scrambles out of bed and as he pulls on his dressing gown he looks out of the window at the familiar scene below and thinks, "Good old milkman. What would we do for breakfast if he didn't get up so early to bring the milk?" Well, he is just about to find out, for when Mrs. Bear tries to pour the milk from the pitcher into the jug all that comes out is an old dried leaf.

and the Wee Man

"I say," cries Rupert, "this is queer!
No milk but just a leaf in here!"

What Rupert says quite mystifies
The milkman. "There's a thief!" he cries.

"What is the milkman thinking of?" exclaims Mrs. Bear, and Rupert is despatched to the dairy with the empty pitcher and the leaf to tell him what has happened. "Not again!" cries the milkman when he is told. And Rupert learns that the Bear family's milk is not the first to vanish. "Just wait till I lay my hands on that thief!" growls the milkman as he refills Rupert's pitcher. Just then Rupert gasps, "There's writing on the leaf!"

"If, as you say, it was a thief,
He's left a message on the leaf."

John Harrold.

RUPERT MAKES A PLAN

The written message gives no clues
To what milk has to do with shoes.

The Bears are not the only lot
Who leaves instead of milk have got.

Says Podgy, "If my leaf's not gone
We'll see if it has writing on."

The pals agree to meet and plan
To trap the milk thief if they can.

"Leave the shoes outside the door," Rupert reads out. But the milkman is too cross and caught up in threatening what's going to happen to "that thief when I get him" to pay attention. So Rupert is left to wonder what it can mean as he walks home. Then suddenly—"Hey, Rupert, has *your* milk been taken now?" He looks up to see his chum Bill Badger calling to him. And with Bill is Podgy Pig. Both the Badger and the Pig families' milk has disappeared in the past couple of days, it turns out, and in each case a leaf was left in the empty pitcher. Bill's has been thrown away but Podgy thinks his may still be in his pocket. "Yes, here it is," he says. "And, you're right, there is writing on it—'2 pairs of shoes for milk and eggs'," he reads out. "Come to think of it, we did have eggs taken too." Rupert has been thinking. "I've an idea of how we might solve this mystery," he says. "Meet me in my garden shed when I've had breakfast."

RUPERT KEEPS WATCH

"Let's leave these shoes outside and see
Who comes. Will someone watch with me?"

"If we lie quietly we're bound
To hear the least suspicious sound."

"Hey, wake up, Bill! We've got to go
And find who's tapping down below."

They throw the front door open wide
And gasp at what they see outside!

"There!" declares Rupert when Bill and Podgy turn up in his garden shed. He points to a very old pair of his Daddy's shoes. The other two look mystified. "Can't you see?" Rupert laughs. "We'll do what the note says. We shall leave these shoes outside the door tonight and wait to see what happens. Now, can you two stay at my house tonight and help keep watch?" Podgy can't but Bill says he's quite sure his Mummy will let him and so she does. So that night,

agreeing that they will stay awake ready to get up the moment they hear anything suspicious, the two pals go to bed and put out the light. For what seems ages they lie listening until they can stay awake no longer ... Suddenly Rupert sits up! Something has disturbed him. Yes, there it goes ... tap-tap-tap. He nudges Bill awake. "Come on," he whispers. "Someone's outside." Silently they creep downstairs. Tap-tap-tap from outside the door. They throw it open. They gasp!

RUPERT'S PLAN WORKS

Amazed, the pals can only stare.
A tiny man is sitting there.

The stranger gives a squeak of fear
Jumps up, darts off and leaves his gear.

"I'm sure our policeman should see these.
So take them down to Nutwood, please."

"A moment can you please spare me?"
A small voice calls from up a tree.

It's hard to say who is more startled, Rupert and Bill or the tiny figure sitting staring at them in dismay with a hammer poised over one of Rupert's Daddy's old shoes. For a long moment no one moves or speaks. Then in the same instant Rupert cries, "Hey!" and the little creature leaps up, scattering shoes, stool and all and disappears into the darkness. Bill wants to go after him but Rupert says, "No, we'd never be able to catch up with him."

"Well, bless my soul!" exclaims Mr. Bear at breakfast as he examines the stuff left behind by the little creature. "A cobbler's toolbox, his stool and his last! Now, what shall we do about this?" "Take them straight down to Constable Growler at Nutwood Police Station," says Mrs. Bear. And so when they have eaten, Rupert and Bill set off for the Police Station. They are passing under a tree when a voice from above says, "Young sirs, spare me a moment, please."

RUPERT OFFENDS THE WEE MAN

The face is one they've seen before—
The little man outside the door.

When stealing's mentioned down he flies
In rage. "What's that you say?" he cries.

Wee People never steal or shirk,
He says, but pay with honest work.

When Rupert's side the Wee Man hears
He suddenly bursts into tears.

There, peering between the branches, is the face of the little cobbler. "Where would ye be off to with my tools and all?" he asks with a smile. "The Police Station?" he repeats when the pals tell him. "And what have the police to do with me and my tools?" he wants to know. "Well," says Rupert, "It rather looks as if you've been stealing milk..." "Wha-a-at?" At the mention of 'stealing' the little figure leaps angrily to the ground. "Stealing?" he yells. "I've never stolen a thing in all my long life, no not one thing!" "B-but..." Rupert begins "No, no buts!" cries the little creature. "Us Wee People give honest work in return for food and drink left out for us..." "But we didn't leave it out for you," Rupert says kindly. "Ye didn't leave it for me?" repeats the other "Oh, dear, oh, dear, what sort of place is it that I've wandered to this time? Oh, I'm a poor Wee Man. I want to go home." And he bursts into tears.

RUPERT'S FRIEND OFFERS HELP

An old friend's servant comes in sight.
The Wee Man disappears in fright.

A language strange the servant speaks
And from the leaves the Wee Man peeks.

"He says that he's inclined to roam
And wants to find his way back home."

The servant volunteers to show
The little man the way to go.

"This is awful," says Bill and Rupert says, "We didn't mean . . ." Then—"Hello, Rupert and Bill!" cries a new voice and round a bend in the path comes the familiar figure of the strange little servant of Rupert's clever friend the Old Professor. In one bound the Wee Man is back among the branches. "Who was that?" asks the servant. He gets three answers at once. "No one at all," says a voice from the branches. "He said something about Wee People," says Bill.

"A Wee Man," says Rupert. "A Wee Man!" repeats the servant and he looks respectful. He looks up and starts talking in a strange, lilting language. The Wee Man replies in the same tongue. The servant says something. They both laugh and the little creature leaps to the ground. "He has wandered a long way and got lost," the servant says. "Now he just wants to go home but doesn't know how. I think I know how, though. Follow me!" And off he scampers up the hill.

RUPERT GOES UNDERGROUND

What is the servant playing at?
He knocks upon a tree "rat-tat!"

A door they didn't see swings wide.
An Elf of Autumn stands inside.

As soon as the Wee Man he sees
The busy Elf sets out to please.

The Elf now ushers them below.
The servant leads and down they go.

Bill and Rupert are pretty good at running but they have a job keeping up with the servant and the Wee Man and they haven't enough breath to spare to ask where they are going. At last the servant stops before a big tree. He raps on the trunk. A door in the tree opens and there stands . . . "An Autumn Elf!" cries Rupert who has met these busy little creatures before. "We need your help," begins the servant. "Too busy at this time!" snaps the Elf. "Too busy for the Wee Man here?" demands the servant. For the first time the Elf notices the little figure. At once he grows respectful. "S-sorry," he stammers. "Of course, we're not too busy for the gentleman." He stands back and ushers the servant and the others into the tree. As they scramble down a flight of stairs after the servant, Rupert whispers to Bill, "Whoever the Wee People are everyone who knows them seems to treat them as if they were very important."

RUPERT TAKES ON A JOB

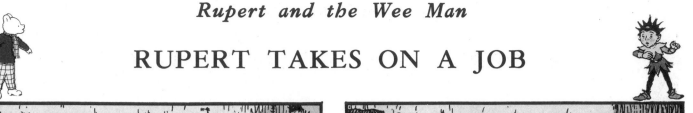

*The Elves' Chief dashes up to say
The Wee Man may use their railway.*

*To vouch, someone must come along,
That though he's strayed he meant no wrong.*

*Bill and the servant can't, and so
It seems that Rupert has to go.*

*"The Wee Man should get off just there,"
The Chief Elf tells the little bear.*

In the Autumn Elves' headquarters underground the covers are being taken off the mist-making machine and yellow and russet tints are being got ready for the trees. But busy as they are, the Chief Elf hurries over when he is told about the Wee Man. "Of course, sir," he says to the Wee Man, "our underground railway also goes under the sea all the way to your home in the Hollow Hill. It is at your service." "Ah," the Wee Man says, "but I shall want one of ye to come with me and explain that I was truly lost, that I wasn't idling and that I truly wanted to come home." Well, who's to go with him? The servant can't. He is helping his master with an important experiment. Bill can't. It's his baby brother's birthday today. So by the time an Elf who has been sent to fetch a map returns, Rupert has agreed to go with the Wee Man. As the others leave he studies the underground railway map with the Chief Elf.

RUPERT DRIVES THE RAILCAR

The Chief explains the railcar will
Take Rupert to the Hollow Hill.

They tear round scary bends and loops.
The Wee Man only laughs and whoops.

The railcar now becomes a boat.
Across the nether sea they float.

A hole, it seems, in the sea-bed
Of the big ocean overhead.

The way to the Wee Man's home in the Hollow Hill seems simple enough and in a moment the Chief Elf is leading the way to the railcar and explaining how to work it. "Just remember to sit facing the other way when you come back," he tells Rupert. Rupert and the Wee Man climb aboard. Rupert pushes the lever forward and off they go, rocketing along at a great rate. At first Rupert is just a bit nervous but the Wee Man plainly loves the speed and whoops and laughs. Rupert holds his breath when they reach the underground sea but the railcar becomes a boat and races on. Suddenly he has to swerve to avoid a deluge of fish and sea-creatures from somewhere above. "Ah, we're under the ocean," the Wee Man says. "And there will be another of those holes in the seabed. I must remember to get word to King Neptune's people about it so that they can get it mended. It's upsetting for the fishes, ye know."

RUPERT GOES INSIDE THE HILL

At last they reach the other side
And from the water smoothly glide.

The symbols strange make Rupert pause.
The Wee Man says he has no cause.

When they have almost reached the top
A voice calls on the pair to stop.

The call comes from a sentry who
Glares fiercely down upon our two.

On the other side of the underground sea Rupert spies a tunnel. "That looks like the one on the map," he says and heads for it. Sure enough a track leads out of the water and into the tunnel. They have not gone far along it when Rupert is aware of a faint glow ahead. "We're just about there," says the Wee Man. "Yes, stop there by those stairs where the glow is brightest." The railcar rolls to a stop. The Wee Man hesitates for a moment before he climbs out, as if he is not very sure what sort of welcome he is going to get at home. As they start up the stairs Rupert wants to know what the strange signs on a stone slab mean. "Just a warning to strangers," says the Wee Man. "But ye'll be all right with me." Rupert wishes the Wee Man sounded a bit more sure as they make their way up through a glowing haze towards a bright light. Suddenly a voice thunders, "Halt!" And there beside a doorway stands a small very fierce guard.

RUPERT INTERRUPTS THE KING

" 'Tis you Wanderer!" cries the guard.
"Oh, you'll be for it, mark my word."

The Wee Man goes ahead alone
Towards the monarch on his throne.

It seems a heavy price he'll pay.
"Oh, please, sir!" Rupert starts to say.

At once there is an angry roar.
He's grabbed and lifted off the floor.

The guard peers at them. " 'Tis you, Wanderer!" he cries. He wags a finger. "Oho, ye'll be for it! And who's this?" He glares at Rupert. " 'Tis a friend to speak up for me," quavers the Wee Man. The guard snorts then blows a note on his horn. He waves them on and Rupert finds himself in a great chamber with a figure on a throne at the far end. The little men crowding the hall make no sound as the two make their way to the throne. "This must be the King of the Wee People,"

thinks Rupert. The Wee Man stops and bows. The silence is frightening. Then the King speaks. He is angry: "You are well-named, Wanderer! Too often now when you should have been working in your own land at your shoe-mending you have gone off wandering and idling, deliberately staying away..." "Oh, please, sir!" Rupert cries. "He *was* working and he *did* get lost..." There is a shocked silence. Then an angry roar and Rupert is grabbed by countless tiny hands.

RUPERT ACCEPTS A DRINK

A blast upon the horn and then
Rupert finds he is free again

Since Rupert took a risk he may,
The King declares, now have his say.

The Wee Man's safe. "And now I think,"
The King says, "you'd enjoy a drink."

"A goblet!" Rupert thinks. "How grand!"
But, oh, the drink's dashed from his hand.

"He spoke! Away with him!" The little men yell as they grab poor Rupert. A horn blares. Silence. The little hands drop away and Rupert is left free and trembling. The King has sounded the horn. He sits and beckons to Rupert. "Approach!" Rupert shuffles forward. "It is the worst sort of disrespect to speak before I command it," declares the King. "But since you have taken the risk of coming here to speak for the Wanderer I am inclined to believe what you may say. Speak!"

"Risk?" wonders Rupert. But he speaks up and tells how hard the Wee Man worked in Nutwood, how he seemed truly to have got lost and wanted to come home. "I believe you," says the King. "It seems the Wanderer is not disobedient, but just silly. He will not be punished." He claps his hands and a guard appears with a goblet. "You must be thirsty, little bear," smiles the King. "Drink!" Rupert raises the delicious smelling drink to his lips only to have it dashed away.

RUPERT IS VERY UPSET

What's happening? What's all this about?
The Wee Man yells, "No drinks! Get out!"

"Oh, how," poor Rupert wracks his mind,
"Could anyone be so unkind?"

He's not a crying sort of bear,
But—gulp—it's really so unfair.

He's too upset to tell the Elf.
He just wants to be by himself.

It is the Wee Man who has dashed the goblet from Rupert's hands. And before anyone else can move he grabs Rupert's arm and angrily hustles him from the hall, past the astonished guard and thrusts him down the stairs, "Away, away!" he shouts. "Ye're neither eating nor drinking here!" Bewildered and shaken Rupert stumbles down to the railcar and clambers into it. "Oh, why?" he keeps asking himself dismally as he heads homewards. "I helped the Wee Man and he grudged me even a drink and threw me out." He can't remember ever having been treated so ungratefully. He's not usually a crying sort of little bear but several times he has to wipe his eyes. And he looks so woebegone when he gets to the end of the line that the Chief Elf is quite upset. "Didn't you get the Wee Man back safely?" he asks anxiously. 'Yes I did," gulps Rupert. "Now I just want to go home." Sadly he leaves the Elves' headquarters.

RUPERT IS HAPPY AGAIN

A voice cries, "Rupert, why so glum?"
The servant on the scene has come.

"If you had drunk in Hollow Hill,
Young Rupert, you would be there still!"

"The Wee Man took a risk, you see,
That you, his new friend, should go free."

So Rupert's laughing at the end
To know he has another friend.

Glumly Rupert trudges away from the entrance to the Autumn Elves' headquarters. "He seemed so nice that Wee Man," he broods. "And then he was so unkind..." "Hey, Rupert, why so glum?" Rupert stops and turns. It is the Old Professor's servant. Dismally Rupert pours out his story and to his absolute astonishment the servant roars with laughter. "Oh, dear," he gasps when he gets his breath back. "The Wee People always try to keep anyone who strays into their Hollow Hill..."

"And you let me go?" cries Rupert. "I thought everyone knew that," grins the servant. "And also that you are safe ... *so long as you take nothing to eat or drink from them!* The Wee Man was taking a big risk stopping you from drinking. That proves just how very grateful he was to you!" "So he really does like me!" cries Rupert. And as he dashes home to tell of his adventure he is laughing and hoping that perhaps he may meet the Wee Man again some day.

RUPERT'S SINGING FLY

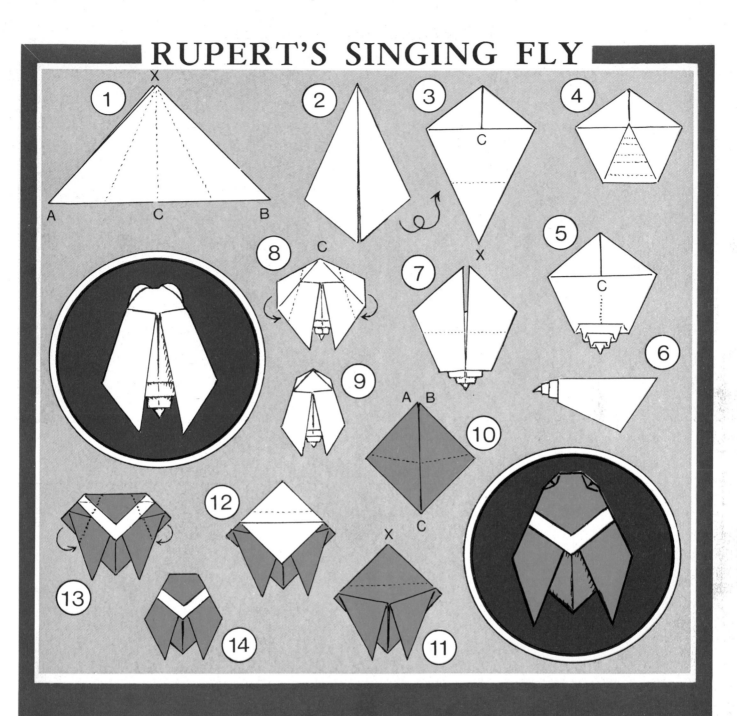

Do you know the little singing or chirping creature called a cicada? Here is a way of making two different ones by paperfolding.

Take a square of thin plain paper and fold it in half by joining opposite points as in Figure 1. Find the middle line by pressing A to B then lay both sides, AX and BX, to CX to make Fig. 2. Turn it over and upside down (Fig. 3) and carry the point X up very slightly beyond C (Fig. 4). Now make five concertina folds of this last flap, according to the dotted lines shown, to make Fig. 5. Fold it in half lengthwise (Fig. 6). Open it as shown in Fig. 7. Bring down the top points, using the new dotted lines, leaving the points apart and taking care that the paper behind falls into equal folds from C (Fig. 8). It may help to

keep a finger on C during that fold. Now fold both sides of the model behind using the new sloping dotted lines (Fig. 9). To finish, push the top of the forehead back and down as in the big drawing, leaving the flaps to serve as eyes.

The second cicada needs a square of paper coloured on one side. Start with Fig. 1, coloured side uppermost, and take A and B up to X (Fig. 10). Bring A and B down by the dotted lines to make Fig. 11. Fold down the top thickness at X to reveal the white (Fig. 12), then bring the second thickness down partly over the first for Fig. 13. Now, using the dotted sloping lines shown, press both sides of the cicada behind the model (Fig. 14). The big drawing shows how to fold a trifle of the top corners to look like eyes.

RUPERT

The snow's been falling all the night.
Now everything is fresh and white.

After snowing all night it is stopping. Rupert who has just finished breakfast looks out at the fresh, crisp whiteness and can't wait to get out to it. "What are you going to do?" asks his Daddy. "Oh, snowballing or building a snowman if I can find any of my pals," Rupert tells him. "Look, here's one of them coming now!" And he runs to open the door to Bill Badger. "Well, thank goodness you're here, anyway!" Bill greets him.

and the Igloo

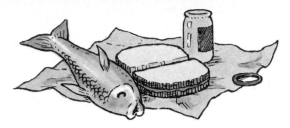

*Rupert finds it is rather queer
That Bill should be relieved he's here.*

*"Just about all our pals are ill,
The poor things have got flu," says Bill.*

Rupert steps outside with Bill. "What do you mean 'thank goodness'?" he asks. "Just that I was beginning to give up hope of finding anyone to play with," Bill says. "Nearly everyone's in bed with flu. The Rabbit twins, the Fox brothers, Podgy and Pong-Ping—all of them ill." "Poor them!" exclaims Rupert. "But I'm all right. Wait here." And he runs in to get his coat and tell his Mummy he is going out.

*He hurries back indoors to say
He's going out with Bill to play.*

29

RUPERT AND BILL WARM UP

"But first an effort must be made.
So here's a shovel and a spade."

So cheerfully the two pals go
To warm themselves by clearing snow.

"A snowman now?" says Mr. Bear.
"Then use these tools," he tells the pair.

Now with their grown-up tools they plan
To build a really big snowman.

When Mr. Bear hears what Rupert and Bill plan to do, he asks, "Do something for me first, will you?" He leads the way to the garden shed and fetches out a spade and a shovel. "Take these and clear the garden path before you start on your snowman. It will get you nice and warm." "Right!" grins Bill. "We'll do it to celebrate the fact that neither of us has got flu!" And in no time at all Rupert and he are shovelling away cutting a path through the snow.

When they report to Mr. Bear that the path is clear he thanks them then adds, "Why don't you hang onto the spade and shovel to build your snowman? They're much better than toy ones for the job." The chums think this is a great idea and off they go making plans for their snowman. "We'll be able to build a jolly big one with these tools," Rupert says "Where shall we build it?" "I know, let's search around for some really deep snow," suggests Bill.

RUPERT MEETS ALGY'S UNCLE

*Then Mr. Trunk they spot and they
Ask him if Edward's fit to play.*

*"Edward," he says, "has cold or flu.
And now, I fear, I've caught it too."*

*"Now who is left to ask?" they sigh.
"Of course, there's Algy Pug. Let's try!"*

*Someone they have not seen before
Answers their knock at Algy's door.*

On their way through the village looking for really deep snow Rupert and Bill spot Mr. Trunk, their pal Edward's Daddy, trudging ahead of them. "That reminds me," Bill says. "I didn't get a chance to call at Edward's house. Maybe he'd like to join us." But when they ask Mr. Trunk he sadly shakes his head. "Sorry, he's in bed with a cold or flu and I rather think I'm catching it too." "What a shame!" Rupert sympathises. "Yes, it's no joke with a nose like mine," sighs Mr. Trunk.

"Well, there's another pal who won't be able to help us with the snowman," Bill says. "Now who else is there who mightn't be ill? Why, Algy Pug! Let's try Algy!" At Algy's house the door is opened by a jolly-looking person the pals have never seen before. "You want young Algy?" he says. "I guess he's out somewhere. I'm his Uncle Percy. I haven't seen him for a while and I'm sorry but I don't know the neighbourhood well enough to guess where you might find him."

RUPERT STARTS A SNOWMAN

He's Algy's uncle. Even so,
Where Algy's gone he doesn't know.

He waves as they start up the hill.
"He'd like to come with us," thinks Bill.

Higher up they are sure they'll find
Snow of the deep and crisper kind.

They work so hard and get so warm
That neither sees the coming storm.

"What are your names?" the stranger wants to know. "Rupert Bear and Bill Badger," he repeats when he has been told. "Right, Rupert and Bill, I'll let Algy know you were looking for him to go play in the snow with you." "Thank you," says Rupert. "Tell him we're going to build a snowman." Algy's uncle grins broadly. "Yeah, a snowman," he says. "I'll surely tell him." He is still smiling as the chums set off. "I have a feeling he'd rather like to come and help us with the snowman himself," says Bill. "Yes, he does seem a jolly sort of person," Rupert agrees. "And he sounds just like my Uncle Grizzly who lives in America. I didn't know Algy had an uncle over there. By the way, I wonder where Algy can have gone." By now the chums are on higher ground and the snow is really thick. "This should do," says Bill and they set to with their shovel and spade. It's such warm work that after a time they shed their coats.

RUPERT TAKES SHELTER

*"We'll make this snowman really tall—
I say, more snow's begun to fall!"*

*The two pals grab their things and race
Towards a better sheltered place.*

*Bill and Rupert now find a tree
And cower for shelter in its lee.*

*The storm is gone. It's then they spy
A figure on a ridge nearby.*

Because they plan to build a really tall snowman Rupert and Bill start by shovelling together a broad pile of snow. "We'll make the snowman as high as we can reach," pants Rupert. "This will be one of the biggest snowmen Nutwood has ever seen." But so absorbed in their work are the two that they don't notice how heavy the clouds have become until the wind rises and snowflakes begin to whirl around them. "Hey, we better find some shelter!" Rupert cries, and grabbing their coats they stumble towards a belt of trees further along the ridge they are on. Buttoning themselves into their coats they take shelter behind a thick tree out of the wind. "I say, I hope this doesn't cover up all our work," says Rupert. "Cheer up!" Bill grins. "All the more snow to work with." Then as suddenly as it began the snowstorm ends and the pals leave the shelter of the trees. But Bill pauses and points. "Look, up on the next ridge! There's someone there."

RUPERT MEETS A STRANGER

*Whoever's up there piling snow
Is no one that they seem to know.*

*"Let's speak to him. Perhaps he will
Let us join in his work," says Bill.*

*He's wrapped up like a furry ball.
The pals can't see his face at all.*

*"Chikki tuk wuk," he grunts and then
Starts patting his snowpile again.*

Rupert looks where Bill is pointing. Outlined against the sky, on top of the next ridge, he can see someone who seems to be very busy piling up snow. "Gosh, he's made a bigger pile than we did!" Bill gasps. "And he seems to have done it with his hands." "Who can it be?" Rupert wonders. "I'm sure it's no one we know. And whatever is he wearing?" As they talk the chums are edging nearer to the strange figure. "Come on, let's speak to him," Bill says. "Maybe he'll join us."

"Ahem!" Rupert coughs as they approach the stranger silently through the snow. Slowly and quietly the figure turns towards them. He is stocky and dressed in thick furs that quite hide his face. He has heavy gauntlets on his hands and there is sacking tied round his feet. "We saw you from the next ridge and wondered if you would like to help with our snowman," Rupert begins. "Chikki tok wuk," grunts the other and resumes patting his snowpile.

RUPERT TRIES TO MAKE FRIENDS

The pals decide how they can tell
The stranger that they mean him well.

They're sure that he will understand
When they join in and lend a hand.

They've got the snowpile really high
When down the hill a chum they spy.

"Can you talk to," they ask the pup,
"This stranger who's so well wrapped up?"

"What language is that?" Bill whispers. "I've no idea," Rupert whispers back. "But it's plain that he doesn't understand English which will make it jolly awkward making friends with him." "Let's try anyway," Bill urges. "We'll show him we mean to be friendly by helping him." "Good idea!" agrees Rupert. "We can work a lot faster with our shovel and spade than he can with his hands." So, smiling broadly, they start to work. The stranger just stands back and watches.

The snowpile is getting really big when Rupert who has stopped to rest for a moment spies a figure climbing the ridge. "Is that Algy? he asks. Bill looks. "No, it's Bingo!" he says. "Hooray! One more pal who isn't ill." In a moment Bingo has joined them. "You're just the chap we need, being as brainy as you are," Rupert greets the clever pup. "This little stranger whose face you can't see for his fur hood, doesn't seem to speak English. See if you can talk to him."

RUPERT'S PAL HAS THE ANSWER

So Bingo tries but he is stuck
When all he gets is "Wikki wuk".

To Bingo it's becoming clear
The sort of stranger they have here.

"I've pictures of his sort, I know.
That's it. He is an Eskimo!"

So what the pals decide to do
Is help to finish the igloo.

Bingo's efforts to make himself understood, though, are no more successful than the others. The stranger just listens in silence then politely bows as far as his thick furs will let him. "Wikki wuk," he grunts and returns to the pile of snow. The others move off a few paces to talk. "That's a jolly big pile of snow he's got there now,' Rupert whispers. "I don't think he means it for a snowman..." "Wait a minute," Bingo breaks in. "I'm getting an idea of what he is."

Rupert and Bill wait for Bingo to go on. "I've seen pictures of people like him in one of my books," he says. "He's an Eskimo, I'm quite sure! I can't imagine, though, what he's doing here in Nutwood. He should be up in the Arctic. And that mound of snow, of course, it's not a snowman at all. It's his igloo. You must have seen igloos in books ... houses made of snow and just the shape he's got there." "Yes, you must be right," Rupert exclaims. "Come on, let's help him some more."

RUPERT SEES AN IGLOO BUILT

While Bill and Rupert join the chore
Bingo stands by and thinks some more.

"That's not the way an igloo's made,"
He says. "Here, let me have your spade."

But when he tries to cut a square
Of snow it crumbles everywhere.

The Eskimo knows best, no doubt.
You build the pile then hollow out.

Rupert and Bill set to once more with shovel and spade. Soon the igloo is even bigger and rounder and they pat the outside until it is hard and smooth. All the time they are doing this the little stranger works on with his hands at his own speed and saying nothing. Suddenly Bingo who has been standing deep in thought interrupts the others. "I've been thinking," he says. "My book shows how igloos are built, and it isn't like this. They're made of blocks of ice. Here, let's

have your spade." Carefully Bingo cuts a square in the surface of the snow. Then he tries to lift it out in a lump. But he no sooner tries than the block crumbles into pieces. "It's too soft," he mutters. "Maybe the little Eskimo knows what he's doing after all." "Yes, look at him now!" Rupert says. "Now I understand. He makes his igloo first and pats it hard so that it won't crumble and then he scrapes out the inside which is what he seems to be doing now."

RUPERT GETS A FRIGHT

*The stranger stands back quietly when
The pals start in to help again.*

*They stop when Bingo breaks the news:
"He needs not one but two igloos."*

*He doesn't understand. He sways.
"Notchi kotchi luk wuk," he says.*

*"Oh, look!" cries Rupert in alarm.
"It seems the stranger's come to harm."*

Now that they are sure they know what he is up to the chums make signs to the little Eskimo that they want to help him scrape out the inside of his igloo. Silently he rises and stands back to let them get on with it. And once more Bingo stands thinking while the others scoop out the snow. "I've had another thought," he announces after a bit. "If he's going to stay here one igloo won't be enough. He'll need one for a bedroom and one for a larder and dining-room.

I do wish we could ask him." Bingo tries to explain to the Eskimo using signs and simple words. But from the depths of the fur hood all that emerges is, "Notchi kotchi, luk wuk." "No use!" Bingo sighs. "We'd best just start building the second igloo and maybe he'll get the idea." Rupert and Bill sigh and Rupert rather wishes that Bingo didn't have quite so many ideas that meant hard work for other people. Then he turns towards the igloo and what he sees alarms him.

RUPERT GOES FOR FOOD

The stranger's crouching in the snow,
Trembling and rocking to and fro.

He's hungry, they decide, and should
Be given the right sort of food.

So off the three pals run to find
Nourishment of a fishy kind.

Grins Uncle Percy, "Whadya know!
You've found a British Eskimo?"

The little Eskimo has collapsed and is crouched in the snow trembling all over. Rupert rushes over to him. "Oh, please...!" he cries. But the little furry figure just goes on trembling in the most alarming way. "What's wrong?" Bill asks. "He must have been taken ill," Rupert says. "I do hope the poor chap hasn't caught that awful flu." "I don't think Eskimos get flu," Bingo says. "After all they live in the cold and damp all the time. I think it's more likely he's just very hungry. He doesn't seem to have any food with him. Let's get him some. Fish, I think. That's what they eat." So off dash the three pals to their homes in search of food. Near his own cottage Rupert runs into Algy's uncle and pours out the story of how Bill and he have found an Eskimo. "A British Eskimo?" grins Uncle Percy. "Well, whadya know!" "No, not British," Rupert says. "He doesn't speak any English at all. He's hungry and we're getting food for him!"

RUPERT'S MUMMY HELPS

He laughs and says, "Gee, you young folk"
And treats the whole thing as a joke.

He'll just keep joking, Rupert sees,
And runs on saying, "Please don't tease."

"A stranger's living on the hill!
An Eskimo! We think he's ill!"

"I've no raw fish at all, I fear.
I'm sure he'll like sardines, my dear."

"Gee!" says Uncle Percy. "The games you kids get up to!" "Games?" Rupert cries. "It isn't a game. That poor little Eskimo is so hungry he's sitting there in the snow trembling all over. We've got to get some food to him. Do *you* know what sort of fish Eskimos like?" "Any old kind of fish," Uncle Percy says heartily. "Raw for preference. Maybe your village store will do you a nice slice of walrus or whale meat!" "Oh, don't tease!" Rupert cries as he hurries on.

Rupert's Mummy is quite taken aback when he rushes up to the front door crying, "Oh, Mummy, there's an Eskimo come to live on the common and we started to help him to build his igloo and then he fell down and started trembling all over and Bingo says the Eskimo needs food and that Eskimos eat raw fish and we're trying to get him some . . ." "Steady on!" laughs Mrs. Bear. "I haven't any raw fish. But I will make sardine sandwiches for him. Everyone likes sardines."

RUPERT'S OFFERING IS ENJOYED

"Let's know at once," cries Mrs. Bear.
"If he gets worse. And do take care."

The stranger's better, that is plain.
He's started scooping snow again.

A head pops out of the igloo.
Says Rupert, "Here's some food for you."

The sandwiches are gobbled up.
"What's happening?" cries the clever pup.

"Now do be careful, dear!" calls Mrs. Bear as she sees Rupert off with his bundle of sardine sandwiches. "Do let Daddy and me know at once if that poor little Eskimo gets any worse." Rupert promises and ploughs on through the snow to the high ridges of Nutwood Common. At last he sees the igloo against the sky. "Hello!" he thinks. "I must be first." For there is no sign of the others. What's more the Eskimo seems to be a lot better. He is busy scooping a hole right through

the igloo. "Hello!" Rupert calls. "I've brought you something to eat. Sardine sandwiches. I don't know if you like sardines but Mummy says she's sure you will . . ." And it looks as if Mrs. Bear is right for the sardine sandwiches vanish into the fur hood and sounds of enjoyment emerge from it. Plainly the little Eskimo is very hungry and just when Rupert is wondering if he should have brought more sardine sandwiches Bingo appears clutching a parcel. "What's happening?" he asks.

RUPERT'S PAL OFFERS RAW FISH

And then Bill dashes up in haste.
He's brought a jar of bloater paste.

Bill's Mummy didn't have raw fish
And thought this was the nearest dish.

The stranger takes the bloater pot,
Then Bingo shows what he has brought.

"Now, this is what they like!" says he.
The stranger seems not to agree.

When Bingo hears about the sardine sandwiches and how the Eskimo gobbled them down, he says, "Oh, dear, I'm sure your Mummy meant well, but I don't think sardine sandwiches are what Eskimos should have. What they really like is . . ." And he starts to undo his parcel. But at that moment up hurries Bill. "Hello," he pants. "Best I could do was a jar of bloater paste. My Mummy didn't have any raw fish but she was quite sure the Eskimo would like bloater paste. Everyone does."

The Eskimo takes the little jar in his gloved hands, but doesn't seem to know what to do with it which isn't surprising since it has not been opened. "Perhaps he likes to eat it with hot buttered toast the way we do," ventures Rupert. "Nonsense!" snorts Bingo. "How on earth would an Eskimo know about hot buttered toast?" He has undone his parcel and in his hands he has a large raw fish. "This is what Eskimos really like!" he says. The Eskimo doesn't seem to agree.

RUPERT DECIDES TO GET HELP

To their dismay the Eskimo
Falls shaking once more in the snow.

They're sure he can't be hungry still.
It really looks as if he's ill.

The stranger then they try to shift
But find he weighs too much to lift.

"Watch him, our shovel and our spade
While Bill and I go down for aid."

With Bingo's raw fish dangling in front of his face the Eskimo collapses again. Down he goes in the snow, feet in the air and shaking all over. "Oh, dear, the poor chap's been taken ill again!" cries Rupert. The Eskimo rolls about in the snow quite alarmingly until he comes to rest face down and shaking. "He can't be hungry!" Rupert cries. "Not so soon after my sardine sandwiches. Oh, how I wish the poor fellow could tell us what's wrong!"

"It's plain he's ill," says Bill. "We can't leave him here." He tries to lift the Eskimo to his feet but gives up when he finds he can't budge him. "I think he's exhausted," Bingo says. "After all he's come all the way from wherever it is Eskimos usually live." "Bill's right," Rupert says. "We can't leave him here. The only thing to do is to get Dr. Lion to have a look at him. You look after the Eskimo and the tools, Bingo, while Bill and I go for help."

RUPERT FINDS DR. LION IS OUT

So off for help the two pals go,
Slipping and stumbling through the snow.

Through Dr. Lion's gate pell mell
They dash and loudly ring the bell.

The doctor's nurse comes to the door.
"The doctor, please!" the pals implore

"He's on his rounds. There's so much flu."
The nurse says. 'Now, what can we do?"

Bingo is not happy about being left to look after the little Eskimo who could be very ill for all he knows. "I don't know much about sick people," he tells Rupert and Bill. "So be as quick as you can." And off go the two chums. "It's all very well telling us to be quick," pants Bill as they stumble through the snow. "But how on earth is anyone supposed to be quick in this." At last, though, they reach the well-trodden Nutwood streets and hurry through Dr. Lion's gateway.

Their urgent knocking at the door is answered by Dr. Lion's nurse. "Oh, dear," she says. "Dr. Lion isn't here. He's out on his rounds and with so many people down with flu goodness knows when he will be back. Is it serious?" "We don't know," Rupert says. "It's an Eskimo and he doesn't speak any English." "An Eskimo!" echoes the nurse. "Oh, my, I don't imagine Dr. Lion knows very much about Eskimo illnesses. Dear me, now I wonder what is the best thing to do."

RUPERT IS GIVEN A STRETCHER

"The only thing to do, it's clear,"
She says, "is bring your ill friend here."

She gives the pals a stretcher then
They start back up the hill again.

"Look here!" the pals hear Bingo shout.
"I can't make this odd stranger out!"

"When you two left remember how
Unwell he seemed. Then see him now!"

As it turns out Dr. Lion's nurse is not quite so fluttery as she seems. After a moment she says, "If you could get your Eskimo friend down here Dr. Lion could have a look at him the moment he gets back. Now, as it happens, we have a small-size hospital stretcher here so why don't you two take it up to the common and bring your Eskimo to the surgery?" And that is how Rupert and Bill find themselves trudging back up to the high common once more carrying a not-very-light stretcher.

"Phew!" gasps Rupert. "I seem to have been up and down this hill all day." "Oh, well, it stops us from feeling chilly," pants Bill who always sees the cheerful side of things. And at last they reach the top of the ridge to find a very agitated Bingo. "I simply can't make out this Eskimo!" he cries. "When you left he was down in the snow trembling all over and soon after you'd gone he was up on his feet and burrowing away inside that igloo like a beaver!"

RUPERT HEARS SOMETHING ODD

He's digging harder than before
And lumps of snow fly out the door.

When Rupert goes to take a peep
The igloo crumbles in a heap.

As they begin to dig him clear
A voice cries, "Get me out of here!"

"Come on, let's get the fellow out
And see what this is all about!"

Sure enough, the Eskimo's feet are sticking out of the entrance to the igloo from which a shower of snow is spraying as the little fellow scoops out the middle of it. Bill and Rupert drop the stretcher gratefully. "I don't understand this Eskimo at all," Rupert declares. "All this falling down and trembling when he doesn't seem to be ill or hungry or tired. It just doesn't make sense." As he speaks he tries to peer inside the igloo to see what is happening and just then it collapses.

Aghast, the three pals crowd round the ruins of the igloo. A small shifting of the snow tells them that underneath it the Eskimo is stirring. "We must get him out. He won't be able to breathe!" Bingo cries. "Yes, come on, start digging!" Bill urges. "No, just a moment! Be quiet!" Rupert orders. Silence. And in that silence a little voice is heard from beneath the snow, "Get me out of here!" "That was English!" Rupert cries. "Let's see what all this is about!"

RUPERT RECOGNIZES A LAUGH

The chums dig fast until they see
The Eskimo and pull him free.

He's crying with the fright he got,
Thinks Bill. But Rupert says, "He's not!"

"That's laughter!" cries the little bear.
"What's more, I'd know it anywhere!"

Back goes the hood. The three pals stare.
It's Algy Pug who's sitting there!

Just as hard as they can Rupert, Bill and Bingo claw at the snow covering the Eskimo and before long they have uncovered his head and shoulders. He seems unable to help himself and it is quite some time before the three can drag him clear of the ruined igloo. As soon as they put him down he sits up and hugs his knees rocking back and forward making strange little sounds. "This is silly!" Rupert bursts out. "When he's in danger he speaks English. Now he makes only odd noises."

"Rupert, I think he's crying!" says Bill which makes Rupert feel ashamed of having been cross. But only for a moment. For when he bends down to the little Eskimo he shouts, "He's not crying! He's laughing! And I know that laugh. Get his hood off!" But before the others can move the hood is pushed back by the Eskimo himself to reveal the beaming face of their chum Algy Pug! And while the others stand and stare with open mouths Algy laughs and laughs and laughs.

RUPERT'S PAL TELLS ALL

"You rascal, Algy!" Rupert cries
When he gets over his surprise.

They pelt him till their arms are sore,
But Algy only laughs the more.

"The fur suit is a gift, you see,
That Uncle Percy brought for me."

"Then you lot came and didn't know
I wasn't a real Eskimo!"

'Oh, dear ... oh, my ... oh, I never!" Algy gasps as he looks at his chums' astounded faces. And he rolls over in the snow gasping with laughter. "Well! You old rascal!" Rupert gets out at last. "How on earth did you do it? Where did you get those furs and how did you keep it up. You've had us fooled for hours!" But Algy can't answer for laughing and at length the others have to laugh too and try to knock some sense into him by pelting him with snowballs.

Snowballs, though, make no impression on that thick fur and after a while Rupert and Bill haul their still giggling chum to his feet and demand an explanation. "Oh, dear!" Algy gasps, tears of laughter running down his face, "My Uncle Percy brought me this Eskimo outfit from Canada. I put it on and went out to build an igloo, then you two turned up ... I never thought I could really fool you ... but, oh, dear ... you were so serious!" And off he goes into another fit of laughing.

RUPERT AND HIS PALS GO HOME

"If you had seen yourselves—oh, my!
I laughed so much I thought I'd cry!"

"All right," says Rupert, "that's enough.
We're off. Let's gather up our stuff."

Still Algy can't resist a tease:
"Do take me on the stretcher, please!"

They gather up their things and go.
They've almost had too much of snow.

"Oh, my, oh, my!" wheezes Algy as he leans against the remains of the igloo. "I haven't the strength to laugh any more. Oh, if you could have seen yourselves when I pretended to speak in Eskimo . . . so solemn . . . and when I pretended to be hungry and Bingo brought me that frightful raw fish . . . well, all I could do was fall down to avoid giving myself away it was so funny!" "All right," says Rupert. "We've been beautifully had! Now let's get home."

Algy still can't help talking about the joke. "All that shivering and trembling," he says. "I wasn't at all unwell. I was laughing and trying hard not to show it. I really thought I should explode! And when you two went and brought back that stretcher . . .! Oh, do carry me home on it, please!" At last he is able to stop laughing and he says, "I know you meant well, chaps, Now, let me help Bingo to carry the stretcher back." And off they trudge towards Nutwood and home.

RUPERT IS ASKED TO TEA

"I'm sorry," Algy tells the nurse.
"I'm glad," she smiles, "that you're no worse."

Then Algy asks the other three,
"Be pals and come on home with me."

Yes, he confesses, he did know
That Algy was the "Eskimo".

"While we have tea I'd like you to
Tell Uncle of our great igloo!"

When Dr. Lion's nurse comes to the door she is fully expecting to have a patient carried in on a stretcher. "What on earth . . .?" she gasps then peers at the group on her doorstep. "Is this your Eskimo?" she asks. "And is he better now?" Algy pushes back his hood and smiles at her. Then he tells her of his joke and says how sorry he is to have caused any trouble. The nurse is a good sort and sees the joke. So it is a cheery group that sets off for Algy's house.

"Well," grins Algy's Uncle Percy who is waiting to greet them, "did you get that slice of walrus for the Eskimo, then?" And he laughs. "So *you* were at the back of Algy's joke!" Rupert cries. "No wonder you were laughing at me when I was so worried about getting the Eskimo something to eat." "Well, come and have tea," says Algy as he removes his Eskimo furs. "It's the least you lot deserve. And you can tell Uncle Percy the whole story of the mysterious Eskimo and his igloo!"

Rupert's Memory Test

Please don't try this memory test until you have read all the stories in the book. When you have read them, study the pictures below. Each is part of a bigger picture you will have seen in a story. When you have done that, see if you can answer the questions at the bottom of the page. Afterwards check the stories to discover if you were right.

NOW TRY TO REMEMBER . . .

1. What is Rupert searching for?
2. How do they get through the tunnel?
3. What does this bird tell Rupert?
4. Whose shoe is this?
5. What was written on this leaf?
6. Who is flying the kite now?
7. Why can't Rupert breakfast now?
8. What has startled Widow Goat?
9. What is in the pot Bill is holding?
10. What is Mr. Bear singing and why?
11. What are these sea-creatures doing?
12. Where will Rupert land up?
13. Something's coming . . . but what?
14. What's going into this sandwich?
15. Who is this? What is his name?
16. What is happening to Bill here?

RUPERT and

On such a day of wind and sun
You need a chum to share the fun.

Sunshine and wind! The sort of day for exploring the countryside around Nutwood; when you almost wish an adventure would happen. "It would be nicer, though if I'd a pal with me," thinks Rupert as he crosses the common. Then—"Hello, Rupert!" The squeaky greeting comes from a small animal under a bush. "Horace Hedgehog!" exclaims Rupert. "I didn't see you." "But I heard you," Horace says. "Thinking aloud."

the Wonderful Kite

Horace the Hedgehog says, "Nearby
You should find Bill. Give him a try."

He hurries down and takes a peep,
And there's Bill fishing—fast asleep!

Rupert laughs: "Yes, I was thinking what a splendid day it is, but not so much fun on your own." "You're in luck," Horace says. "Bill Badger is fishing near here. Try him." Rupert thanks Horace and heads for the stream. Sure enough, there's Bill on a plank over the water, fishing-rod in hand . . . fast asleep. "Lazy beggar," Rupert chuckles. "I'll show him." He steals up, lifts out the line and fixes his handkerchief to it.

So Rupert steals down to the brook
And ties his hankie to Bill's hook.

53

RUPERT CHASES A HAT

"I say, I've got a bite!" Bill cries,
Then almost falls in with surprise.

"In fact that fishing was a bore,"
Bill says. "Come on, let us explore!"

As often happens in such gales,
Over a hedge someone's hat sails.

It bowls along as if alive
Until Bill traps it with a dive.

Rupert tugs the handkerchief. Bill wakes with a start. "I've got a bite!" he cries. He pulls in his line and finds . . . a handkerchief. "What . . .?" he begins then swings round, nearly falling off the plank when Rupert bursts out laughing. But being Bill he shares the joke and when Rupert asks him to come exploring he says he'd love to and that he was getting bored anyway. So off they go, arm in arm, both with a feeling that some adventure lies ahead.

As the pals press on the wind gets stronger. Bushes flail and trees shake. "This sort of wind brings down chimney pots!" Bill says. "And look, there goes one now!" Rupert sees the round, black thing soar over the bushes. "No, it's a hat!" he cries. "After it, Bill!" Laughing, they chase the hat across the field. Each time they think they have it a gust blows it out of reach again. Then at last Bill catches it with a tremendous flying tackle.

RUPERT MEETS THE HAT'S OWNER

Bill tries the hat. It hides his eyes.
"Let's play a game then!" Rupert cries.

Then at the gate a man appears.
It's his hat they have, Rupert fears.

The man's not cross. He doesn't mind.
"You caught my hat," he says. "How kind!"

"For saving my old hat from harm
I'll show you two around my farm."

"Go on, Bill, try it on!" Rupert grins. Bill jams the hat over his head. "I can't see a thing!" he laughs with the brim resting on his nose. "I know, then!" cries Rupert. "Let's play blind man's buff." But they have hardly begun to play when a shout stops them. Bill whips off the hat. A man is waving at them. "I say, I rather think it's his hat we've got," Rupert whispers as the man beckons to them. "Come on, we'd better take it back to him quick."

Wondering if the man saw them playing about with his hat, Rupert and Bill approach nervously. But as they get near they see that he is smiling. If he has seen them larking with his hat he doesn't mention it. Instead he says, "That was kind of you to catch my hat. It's old but I'm fond of it." He turns out to be a farmer and when he learns that the pals like farms he shows them around his. When they have seen everything he asks, "Hungry, eh? Then how about some lunch?"

RUPERT IS GIVEN THE KITE

They lunch and then he tells the two,
"Up here I've a surprise for you."

"Oh what a mess!" he says. "Oh dear!
But I'm quite sure it's somewhere here."

"Yes, here it is, my good old kite!"
The pals accept it with delight.

As off they go their friend reveals
The kite has some strange power, he feels.

After a delicious lunch the farmer says, "Now I have a surprise for you. Follow me." He leads Rupert and Bill through the old farmhouse and up a twisty flight of stairs to a loft, cluttered with all sorts of things. "Now, I'm sure it's hereabouts somewhere," he mutters, gazing around at the mass of trunks and crates and boxes. The pals exchange looks. What can he be looking for? Then—"Aha! There it is!" cries the farmer and plunges among some packing cases.

What he produces is a kite. It's a good one, old but beautifully made. "Here you are," he says. "A 'thank-you' present for saving my hat." The delighted chums thank him over and over as they carry the kite down from the loft. "Just one thing," says the farmer. "I've heard it said this old kite has magic powers. I don't know for sure, but it's led me into one or two strange adventures." Excitedly Rupert and Bill rush outside to try their new present.

RUPERT LOSES THE KITE

By now the wind has grown so strong,
Quite helpless, Rupert's dragged along.

Bill lends a hand. They tug and, oh!
The kite string snaps and down they go.

And off it soars, their lovely kite!
They try to keep the thing in sight.

They saw it come down in some trees,
And think they'll find the spot with ease.

How that kite can fly! In the strong wind it soars like a great bird, dragging Rupert along, panting and stumbling with Bill racing behind. Soon they are on high ground where the wind is even stronger. "I—I can't hold it on my own!" pants Rupert. "Come on, Bill, give me a hand with it!" Bill grabs hold of the line and the two throw their full weight backwards. For a moment it seems that they can hold the kite, then—ping!—the line snaps.

Off soars the kite, free of the line. "For goodness' sake, don't lose sight of it, Bill!" Rupert shouts as they pick themselves up. From the top of the hill they watch their new present dwindle into the distance ... then suddenly it plunges into a wood. "After it!" cries Rupert. "I think I saw where it came down." They race down the hill and into the wood. But there, in among the thick trees and the bushes, finding the kite doesn't seem nearly so easy.

RUPERT IS LED TO THE KITE

*But no, the wood's too dense and they
Soon find that they have lost their way.*

*Just then they see a bird alight.
It knows where they can find their kite.*

*"Behind that wall's a garden fair.
And you will find your kite in there."*

*But when at last the door swings wide
An ugly old man stands inside.*

Deeper and deeper into the woods push the two chums. At last Bill stops, leans against a tree and wipes his forehead. "I'm lost. I've no idea which way we're going even. I don't think we're going to find the kite, do you?" Glumly Rupert shakes his head. "Kite?" says a tweetery voice. "Are you two looking for a kite?" The speaker is a bird perched on a tree stump. At once the pals are alert again. "I've seen a kite," says the bird. "Follow me. I'll show you where."

Hardly able to believe their good luck, Rupert and Bill follow the bird through the trees. It stops at last before a high stone wall with a door in it. "Your kite fell into the garden behind this wall," chirps the bird. "Good luck!" Good luck? That's an odd thing to say, Rupert thinks. But the bird has already gone. Now Bill reaches for the bell-pull beside the door and tugs. After what seems a long time the door is opened by an ugly, scowling old man.

"I'll have no strangers nose about
In here," the old man snarls. "Get out!"

The two chums turn and seem to flee.
But stop and hide behind a tree.

They circle all around that wall.
But everywhere it's far too tall.

"Bill, just a moment!" Rupert cries.
"Our way in through that tunnel lies."

"M—may we come in and get our kite?" Rupert quavers. "Come in?" repeats the old man, and he scowls more fiercely than ever. "Come in? Never! You get away from here and stay away. Don't want any nosey strangers prowling round here. Now get out!" And to the pals' alarm he produces a stick from behind his back and waves it at them. They turn and run ... but only as far as a big tree behind which they hide until the old man goes growling back into the mysterious garden.

"Let's see if we can find some other way of getting inside," Rupert says. So they set off following the wall. But everywhere it is high and even if they could climb it they can see they would be stopped by the spikes on top. "It looks as if we've lost our kite for good," Bill says dismally. And it is just at that moment that Rupert spies a possible way in—a tunnel that allows a small stream to run under the wall and into the garden.

RUPERT SAILS THROUGH

"Yes, that's it, Rupert! Good for you!"
Bill cries. "But how do we get through?"

No need for them to swim or wade,
They'll use the tree trunk as an aid.

"I'll make the log secure. We may
Just need it to come back this way."

They board the log, they cower low,
Then underneath the wall they go.

"But how do we get through it?" Bill wants to know. "Swim? We could. It looks pretty short." "I've a better idea," Rupert says. "That log over there." He points to a length of tree trunk on the bank. "Give me a hand to get it into the water." "You mean we float through the tunnel on it?" Bill exclaims. "I say, that is a good idea!" The log is big and old but the chums pushing together manage to roll it to the water's edge. Then in it goes and Rupert scrambles onto it to hold it steady. "Just a minute," Bill says. "We may need this to get back out again so we must make sure it doesn't float away." From his pocket he produces his long fishing line. One end of it he ties to the log, the other he knots around a tree. "Good thinking, Bill" says Rupert. Now Bill joins Rupert on the log. They lie flat and the log begins to drift through the tunnel. The light at the far end gets brighter and then they are back in the sunlight—and the garden.

RUPERT SEES THE HUGE FLOWERS

Almost the first thing that they see—
Their kite stuck halfway up a tree.

Before they can get to their kite
That ugly old man comes in sight.

The old man's gone so on they push,
But look! A primrose like a bush!

They round a corner. Stop! And stare.
A little girl is standing there.

Almost as soon as they emerge from the tunnel the chums spot their kite. It is caught in the branches of a tree. "Come on, let's get it and get out of here before that old man turns up," urges Bill. They jump ashore and scramble up the bank to the tree. They are almost there when Rupert suddenly grabs Bill's arm and drags him into the bushes. Stumping up a path, looking surlier than ever, comes the ugly old man. The chums hold their breath.

Luckily for them the old man is too intent on wherever he is going to look in their direction. When they are quite sure he has gone they come out of hiding. They pause to look around. "This is a pretty strange garden," Rupert whispers. "Look at the size of the flowers. This primrose is like a young tree." "I don't think I like this," Bill breathes. "Come on." And so they steal quietly on. Suddenly they stop. Ahead of them a girl is gardening. She turns and stares.

"You two have no right here, you know!
You're trespassing!" she cries. "Now go!"

Then to the chums' dismayed surprise
The little girl breaks down and cries.

"My plants all grow too big and fast,"
She says. "And none of them will last."

As if to prove she doesn't lie
A little tree sweeps Bill up high.

The girl and the chums stare at each other in silence for a moment then the girl cries, "You have no right here! You're trespassing! How dare you!" She seems really upset and the chums have a hard time of it explaining that they mean no harm and that they only want to get their kite back. Suddenly the girl stops being angry. "I am sorry!" she gulps. "But I'm so upset. You see, I'm Mary Quite Contrary and I love my garden but nothing will grow properly." And she weeps.

"Do tell us about it," Rupert begs. "Perhaps we can help." Mary dries her tears and manages a little smile. "That's nice of you," she says. "I don't think you can but . . ." And she explains that her flowers either come up small and withered or quite huge and that the very big ones last no time at all before they wither and die. Just then, as if to prove what she is saying, a small tree behind Bill starts growing so rapidly that it catches his coat and lifts him off his feet.

"Hey, get me out of here!" Bill bawls.
The tree is shaken. Down he falls!

"You sneaked in after all, you two?
Just let me get my hands on you!"

"He's our gardener, a lazy one,"
She tells the two chums as they run.

The girl's grandfather says they might,
Because it's so late, stay the night.

Up, up goes the tree with poor Bill struggling helplessly. "Hey, get me down!" he cries. Like an answer to his pleas a large hand emerges from the bushes, grasps the tree's trunk and shakes it hard. Bill lands with a very nasty bump and the others are helping him up when the bushes part and the scowling face of the old man appears. "So you sneaked in after all!" he snarls. "Well, just wait till I lay hands on you." As he starts through the bushes Mary grabs the chums' hands.

"Quick, we must hide," she cries and she drags them off along a maze of paths with the old man lumbering behind. "He's the gardener here," Mary pants. "But he never seems to do any work. My grandfather thinks he is honest and won't get rid of him ... Oh, here is my grandfather." The old gentleman Rupert and Bill are introduced to listens politely to their story of the kite. Of course, they may have it back, he says. But it is late. They must stay the night.

They sup and then he shows the pair
The little room that they're to share.

A shadow on the window pane:
The gardener's on the prowl again.

They keep the old man's lamp in sight
And follow him into the night.

They stop. They listen. And they stare.
He's gone into those bushes there.

After a delicious supper Mary's grandfather, who turns out to be a jolly as well as kindly old gentleman, shows Rupert and Bill to their bedroom. It is small but very comfortable. As the pals get ready for bed they talk and they agree that something very odd is going on in Mary's garden. "I'm sure it has something to do with that old gardener," Rupert muses. "He was terribly anxious that no strangers should see inside the garden..." "Sh-sh!" interrupts Bill. "There he goes!" He points to a shadow passing their window. "He's up to no good I'm sure," Rupert whispers. "Come on, let's follow him." Silently, swiftly the chums slip out of the house. They are in time to see the gardener, clutching a lantern, disappear behind a big tree. On tiptoe they scurry after him. But when they reach the tree there is no sign of him. There is, though, a rustling from a nearby clump of bushes. "He's in there!" breathes Bill.

They must press on, the two pals see,
If they're to solve the mystery.

Deep in the bushes they have found
Some steep steps that go underground.

They must go on so down they go
And find a weird cave there below.

They find the gardener in that hole
Mixing up powders in a bowl.

The chums stand quite still until the rustling in the bushes stops. "I'm sure the secret is in there somewhere," whispers Rupert. "If we want to discover it we've got to go in." Bill nods and in they plunge. Almost at once they see a bright light in the middle of the clump and make for it. It is coming from a hole in the ground—a hole with steps leading down. The chums exchange looks. They nod and very cautiously Rupert leads the way underground.

What they find at the foot of the steps is the most astonishing sight—a great cavern seemingly full of pillars. The pillars, though, turn out to be the roots of great trees. "We're under the woods," breathes Bill as they pick their way between the roots. Suddenly they freeze in their tracks then duck for cover behind an especially big root. Ahead of them the gardener is standing at a bench covered in bottles and jars. Carefully he is measuring powders into a bowl.

RUPERT UNCOVERS THE SECRET

He's done at last and starts to go.
That he's been seen he doesn't know.

"We'll take some samples of this stuff.
Two bottles should be quite enough."

The powder that he made is thrown
Where tiny seedlings have been sown.

A plant that they could barely see
At once shoots up, tall as a tree.

Cowering behind their root Rupert and Bill keep watch on the gardener for what seems a long time. At last he appears to be satisfied with his work. He corks his various bottles and jars then with his bowl starts for the stairs back to the surface. When they are quite sure he has gone the chums leave their hiding-place and approach the bench. "Before we go we better take samples of this," Rupert says. "We may need them." They take two small bottles then set off after the gardener.

Back in the garden Rupert and Bill stop for a minute and listen. When they can hear the old gardener moving about they make for the sound. They find him beside one of Mary's flower-beds. As they crouch behind a bush in the darkness they hear him mutter, "This should do the job, heh, heh!" Then he sprinkles some of the powder from his bowl onto a tiny plant. Almost at once the plant shoots to a great height and bursts into bloom. "Now we know!" Rupert whispers.

RUPERT SHOWS THE PROOF

Then silently they steal away.
They'll tell what they have seen next day.

"This powder," Rupert says, "will show
How all your plants are forced to grow."

He finds a tiny pimpernel
To demonstrate the old man's spell.

They gasp. They can't believe their eyes.
The plant's now an enormous size.

Delighted at having solved the mystery of Mary Contrary's garden Rupert and Bill hurry back to the house and their beds. First thing next day, they agree, they will tell Mary's grandfather. And so straight after breakfast next morning they go to the old gentleman and pour out their story. Being a very fair as well as a kindly man he can't believe that his old gardener could be up to no good. "Then, please, sir, at least come and see what his powder does," Rupert pleads.

The old man agrees, but not very willingly, and out they go into the garden. In the middle of a path Rupert spies a tiny pimpernel. "This will do," he says. He sprinkles it with some of the powder. In a moment it is a towering bush. "The villain!" cries Mary's grandfather when he has got over his surprise. "Plainly he has invented this powder so that he doesn't have to work at making things grow, even though he knows the poor flowers will die quickly!"

RUPERT GETS HIS KITE BACK

But now they see the tragic plight
Of what grew up so fast last night.

The gardener is shown the door.
"Be off!" he's told. "Return no more."

And so at last the pals are free
To get their kite down from the tree.

"What this log?" Rupert laughs. "Oh, dear!
That is how Bill and I got here."

Now Rupert leads the way to the plant Bill and he saw grow so rapidly last night. It lies shrivelled on the ground. "Oh, this is too much!" cries Mary's grandfather. "I shall dismiss him at once!" When the gardener is told that his mischief has been discovered he tries at first to bluster and lie but he soon sees that he is wasting his time. "Go!" orders Mary's grandfather. "And remember that a beautiful garden can only be created by hard work and loving care."

With the mystery cleared up and the gardener banished, Rupert and Bill remember what brought them to the garden in the first place—the kite. With the old gentleman's permission Rupert, who is very good at climbing, shins up the tree and gets the kite. Luckily it is quite undamaged. Then something catches the old gentleman's eye. "What is that log doing in our stream?" he asks. "Oh, dear," chuckles Rupert. "That's how Bill and I got in here past the gardener.

RUPERT SETS OFF FOR HOME

The pals are taken to some stairs
And shown a boat they're told is theirs.

But now it's time to leave and so
They say their thanks and off they go.

The trees are dense, the light is dim
As down the little stream they skim.

Something, they feel, is not quite right.
The gardener has them in sight.

"Come with me," says Mary's grandfather with a smile, and leads the way downstream. He stops beside a neat little boat moored at the foot of some steps. "That is your reward for helping me," he says. "I'm sure you will find it a lot more comfortable than a log." Of course, Rupert and Bill want to set off at once to try their new boat but Mary makes them wait until she has made sandwiches to eat on their homeward journey. Then with a last wave the two pals set off.

After the garden the woods seem gloomier and thicker than ever. "I hope we can reach Nutwood by keeping to the stream," says Bill. "I don't fancy leaving the boat and having to go through the woods again." Nor does Rupert and it isn't just because the woods look so uninviting. He has a feeling that they are being watched. And he is right. For tracking them along the bank, dodging from tree to tree, is the old gardener, who is determined to get his own back.

At last they reach a sunlit lake
And Rupert says, "Let's have a break."

They find a place that seems just right
And go ashore to have a bite.

They settle down to eat their lunch.
But someone steals up as they munch.

The pals are taken by surprise.
"You're going to pay!" the gardener cries.

Soon after Bill takes a turn at paddling the boat the stream flows out into a broad sunlit lake. "That's a bit better," Rupert says. "I didn't like that stretch through the woods at all." By now the pair are beginning to feel hungry. "Head for that old tower," Rupert says. "We can picnic there." Near the tower they find a flat stretch where they can beach their boat. They take their things out of it, the kite, the paddle and the sandwiches and settle down to rest and eat. But as they munch and chat about their adventure they little realise that it is not over. For stealing through the bushes behind them comes the gardener who has followed them round the shore. Suddenly when they are least expecting it, he springs. He grabs them by their arms. "Aha!" he snarls. "You didn't think, did you, that I'd let you away with losing me my job like that. No, no, I'm going to make sure you pay for that!"

RUPERT IS PUT TO WORK

He tells the pals, "You'll come with me."
In vain they struggle to break free.

"I make my powders here, and you
Shall have the dirty work to do!"

He locks them in this dismal hole
To carry sacks and shovel coal.

And when at length the man returns,
He has their paddle which he burns.

Rupert and Bill wriggle and squirm but they cannot break free of the gardener's grip and they find themselves being dragged up the overgrown path that leads to the old tower. The gardener bundles them inside then slams and locks the door with a key he takes from his pocket. They don't have to wonder long how he comes to have a key to the tower. "Bad luck you chose to stop near here," he gloats, waving the key at them. "This is the place I make my magic gardening powder."

He grins at the dismay on the pals' faces. "Now you're going to do all the hard part of that work like shovelling coal for the furnace." And hard work it is, both hot and dirty. After a while the gardener goes off somewhere. "We must try to get outside, even if only for a moment," Rupert whispers. "Then we can get away in the boat." But their captor has thought of that too. When he returns he is carrying their paddle. "Just in case . . ." he growls, and puts it in the furnace.

RUPERT SEES BILL'S PLAN FAIL

They're ordered to a loft to sleep.
So, tired and grimy, up they creep.

Bill pulls a bottle out, says, "Look,
Here's half the growing stuff we took!"

"With luck," he says, "there may well be
Somewhere down there a tiny tree."

But no strong tree springs up, alas!
The only thing that grows is grass.

At last the day draws to a close and the pals are told they can stop work. "You two sleep up in the loft where you can't play any tricks," the gardener tells them and makes them climb to the top of the tower. Rupert is still clutching the kite. "Get a good night's sleep," the old man says, grinning unpleasantly. "You will be working even harder tomorrow." When the man has gone, locking them in, Rupert slumps onto a box looking glum. But Bill seems excited. From a pocket inside his jacket he produces one of the bottles of the gardener's growing powder they took the night before. "This makes plants grow very fast, doesn't it?" he begins. Rupert nods. Bill crosses to the window and Rupert follows. "So if there's a tiny tree growing under this window . . ." Bill says, sprinkling the powder on the ground below. "It will grow up here and we can climb down it!" Rupert cries. But there is no tree. Just a lot of useless grass.

RUPERT HAS A BETTER IDEA

*"Cheer up!" cries Rupert. "I've a plan
By which we might escape that man."*

*"Bill, hold it steady while I write
A message telling of our plight."*

*They cut the string. The kite goes free.
And with it goes their rescue plea.*

*Both pals feel they have done their best
To get away and now can rest.*

Poor Bill is terribly upset that his clever plan has come to nothing, especially as he has used almost half the powder. He is so upset that Rupert starts thinking doubly hard about a way to get out of the tower. Then—"I've got it!" he cries. "The kite, of course! We'll write a message on it and let it fly away. Someone is bound to find it and come to our rescue." Bill cheers up at once and holds the kite steady while Rupert writes on the kite with the stub of pencil he always carries in a pocket just in case. Then they carry the kite to the window. Good! The wind is still high. Rupert launches the kite and waits till it is pulling strongly before he cuts the line with the knife he also always carries in his pocket just in case. Away goes the kite high over the trees. Now that there is a chance of someone learning of their plight and coming to help them the pals feel a lot more cheerful and settle down on a bed of straw and sacks.

RUPERT GETS A FLYING MESSAGE

They sleep right through until it's light.
And look! Outside the tower—the kite!

"Yes, Rollo's trying hard to steer
So we can pull the kite in here."

They reach right out and grab the thing.
Its message says, "Pull in the string".

They haul the string and find their friend
Has tied a stout rope to the end.

"Rupert! Quick, look!" Rupert is wakened from a deep sleep by Bill's urgent cry. His chum is on his feet and pointing excitedly at something outside the window. "The kite!" he gasps. "It's back!" And he leaps up to join Bill at the window. "Bill," he cries, "it's Rollo!" There, some way from the tower is one of their friends, Rollo, the gipsy boy. Skilfully he is keeping the kite near their window. "I'm sure he wants us to pull it in," Rupert says. "Get ready to grab it when it comes near enough." A moment later the kite comes into reach. Bill catches hold of it and pulls it inside. "Look!" Rupert says, "He's rubbed out our message and written something in its place . . . 'Pull in the kite string'." They lean out of the window and wave to show that they have understood. The string, when they start to pull it, is surprisingly heavy. They soon see why. Rollo has attached it to a length of sturdy rope which is coiled beside him.

RUPERT AND HIS PALS FLEE

They fix the rope and down they go
To Rollo waiting there below.

He says he found the kite last night
And came as soon as it was light.

The old man's gone out, but he may
Be back soon so they speed away.

Alas, it looks as if they're caught!
He's come back sooner than they thought.

Rupert and Bill pull the end of the rope into the loft and tie it securely to a bolt set in the wall. "Right, down we go," Rupert says. "You first, Bill." Bill swings himself out onto the rope and Rupert follows, but not before he has cut loose their precious kite to bring with him. As they reach the ground Rollo runs up to meet them. "I found your message yesterday evening," he says, "and came round here at first light. I thought you were never going to wake up. That old man went off somewhere very early and as soon as he was out of sight I started flying the kite." "Well, we better be off before he comes back," Rupert urges. "Right!" Rollo says. "Let's make for our gipsy camp. It's quite near and he will never think of looking there." They set off at a run. "I thought we were never going to escape," Bill pants as they go. "But we have." Bill has spoken too soon. An angry shout! And there is the gardener bearing down on them.

RUPERT FOILS THE GARDENER

Rupert turns and hopes he can
With growing powder stop the man.

It causes him enough delay
To let the three pals get away.

The only route that they can take
Is by their boat across the lake.

"The gardener burnt our paddle so
We'll have to use our hands to row."

The old man has come back sooner than they hoped! For an instant they stare at each other then as the gardener makes a rush at them our three turn and flee. But they are running in the direction of the lake and the gardener is gaining on them. Rupert is aware of something bulky in his pocket that is making running more difficult. It's the bottle with the rest of the growing powder Bill had. He remembers picking it up as he left the tower ... Brainwave! He stops, uncorks the bottle and scatters its contents on the ground. Almost at once the grass springs up like a jungle, halting their pursuer and giving the chums precious seconds to reach the shore and the boat. Rupert and Bill scramble aboard while Rollo pushes the boat out. As he follows the other two into it the gardener bursts out of the long grass yelling angrily. "Paddle with your hands, Rollo!" Rupert cries. "That man burnt our paddle to stop us escaping."

76

RUPERT PUTS THE KITE TO WORK

Although they've left the man behind,
To row by hand's too hard, they find.

"The answer," Rupert cries, "is clear.
It's with us in the boat, right here!"

Because the wind's still blowing strong
The kite can pull the boat along.

So there is no need for an oar.
They glide towards the distant shore.

The push Rollo gave the boat was a hefty one and carries the three chums far enough from the shore to leave the gardener dancing in helpless rage. And it's as well he did push hard, for although the three paddle furiously with their hands they make sadly little progress and soon they are exhausted. On shore the gardener is still hopping about in the hope the boat without a paddle may drift back towards him. Then Rupert suddenly laughs. "We are asses!" he cries. "We have the answer right here in the boat with us." The other two sit up and stare. "This!" Rupert declares and produces the kite which Bill and he have been careful not to leave behind despite all the excitement. While the others watch he ties the kite's string to the ring in the prow of the boat. Then he launches the kite which at once is picked up by the strong wind. And over the lake it goes towing the boat behind it. "Ah, now, this is the way to travel!" chuckles Rollo.

RUPERT IS HOME AGAIN

And now the kite, so it would seem,
Is going to take them up a stream.

"I thought I recognised this brook,"
Rupert exclaims, "There's Nutwood! Look!"

Not many minutes pass before
They moor their boat and jump ashore.

Then Rupert's parents hurry out
To see what this is all about.

As the kite pulls the boat over the lake the pals learn how to steer it. All they need do is trail their hands in the water. And it is as well they can steer when they reach the stream on the far side of the lake with all its twists and turns. All thoughts of going to the gipsy camp have had to be forgotten, but something even safer lies ahead. Quite suddenly Rupert finds that he recognises bushes and trees and stretches of bank. "We're near Nutwood!" he cries. "What a bit of luck! This stream runs right past the bottom of our garden!" And in no time at all they are mooring the little boat just outside Rupert's back garden gate while Mr. and Mrs. Bear hurry down to see what all the fuss is about. "Where on earth have you been?" Mr. Bear wants to know. "Mummy and I have been so worried." "Just wait till I tell you all the exciting things we've been doing!" Rupert says as Podgy, Algy and Willie run to welcome him.

RUPERT SHOWS PODGY

Now Rupert tells how Bill and he
Cleared up the garden mystery.

But Podgy scoffs at what he hears.
"What? Magic powder? No!" he jeers.

Right! Podgy shall see how it grows.
What's left is scattered round his toes.

The last laugh is on Podgy who
Peers out like something in a zoo.

At each turn of Rupert's tale his listeners gasp. All of them, that is, except Podgy Pig who is always too ready to believe that people are making things up; maybe because he makes things up himself sometimes. Whenever Rupert says anything about the magic growing powder Podgy makes a great show of bursting out laughing. "Oh, come on, Rupert!" he guffaws. "You don't expect us to believe that, do you?" At last Rupert has had enough of Podgy's rudeness. He has kept the bottle which contained the magic growing powder because it still has a little left in it. Now he opens it and sprinkles the grains of powder on the ground in front of Podgy. "Here, what are you doing?" Podgy cries. 'What's that stuff you're throwing about . . . I say, what's happening? Look at the grass . . . get me out of here!" For now the grass has sprung up around him and he is peering out of it like something in a zoo. And how the others laugh at his antics!

79

RUPERT

*"Ask Widow Goat to come to tea
When you go to the shops for me."*

It is Christmas Eve and Mrs. Bear is making a last check of her supplies to make sure she has all she needs. "Just a few small things to get from the shop," she says, "so perhaps you'll get them for me, Rupert." In fact, Rupert is glad of the chance of a trip into the village and sets of cheerfully armed with a shopping list. "By the way," Mrs. Bear says as he leaves, "drop in at Widow Goat's and invite her round to tea."

and the Cuckoo Clock

So Rupert sets out with his list,
But doesn't see the rising mist.

The fog is now so thick that he
The Widow's house can hardly see.

So off Rupert goes, studying the shopping list as he heads for Widow Goat's cottage. What he does not notice is the thick fog creeping up behind him. By the time he is aware of it Widow Goat's cottage is in sight and he doesn't think it is worthwhile turning back. He approaches the cottage door and knocks. He waits. But nothing happens. He knocks again, but still no answer. Then from inside he hears a strange little sound.

He knocks. A little sound he hears.
But no old Widow Goat appears.

81

RUPERT MEETS THE HOARSE BIRD

"Perhaps," he thinks, "I should explore."
And so he gently tries the door.

The sound comes from a cuckoo clock.
His nearness gives the bird a shock.

But Rupert coaxes it to speak
And learns the fog's made its throat weak.

"Some medicine you clearly need,"
Says Rupert and goes off at speed.

"I better have a look inside just in case there is something wrong," thinks Rupert. The silence broken only by that little noise worries him. He pushes open the door and steps inside. The place is empty. "Widow Goat?" he calls gently. Silence. Then suddenly the curious sound again. He spins round to where it comes from. And it seems to come from a cuckoo clock where the cuckoo is peering out of his little door. When it catches sight of Rupert it retreats, shutting the door.

Rupert climbs onto a chair so that his face is level with the clock's. "What's wrong?" he asks gently. "You don't sound well." The little door opens and the cuckoo looks out. "Oh, dear!" it croaks. "It's this English winter fog. It gets into my throat so. If I don't get some medicine soon I shall have to give up telling the time." "You poor thing!" Rupert exclaims. "I'm on my way to the shops. I'll try to get something for you." And off he goes into the thickening fog.

RUPERT GETS THE MEDICINE

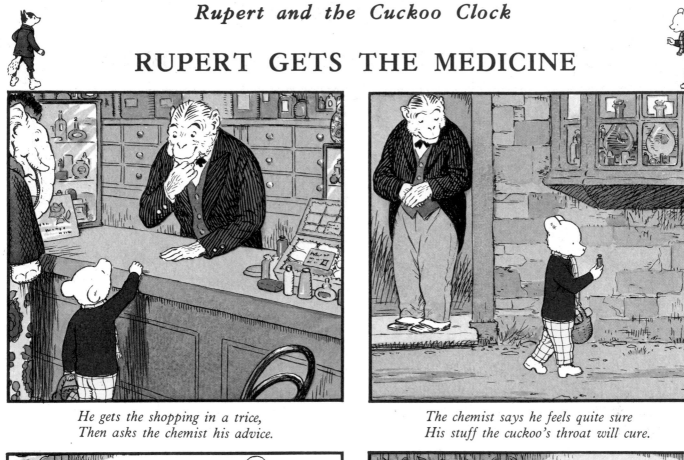

He gets the shopping in a trice,
Then asks the chemist his advice.

The chemist says he feels quite sure
His stuff the cuckoo's throat will cure.

"The cuckoo clock of Widow Goat,"
He says, "has got a husky throat."

"Now," Rupert cries, "I must make haste!"
Says Mr. Bear, "Let's have a taste."

As soon as he has done his Mummy's shopping Rupert hurries round to Mr. Chimp the chemist. "Something for a cuckoo with a husky throat?" repeats Mr. Chimp when Rupert has explained what he wants. "H'm, let's see . . . unusual, I must say, but I think I can let you have something that will do." And off he goes to make up a special mixture. When he hands it to Rupert he warns, "Be sure to let the cuckoo have only a drop at a time. It is very strong."

"What's that little bottle you have there?" asks Mrs. Bear when Rupert returns with her shopping. So Rupert explains how Widow Goat was not at home and how he found the cuckoo with the sore throat and got some special medicine for it from the chemist. Mr. Bear who has heard all this says, "Medicine for a cuckoo's sore throat? Whatever next. I must try this." "Well, only a sip," says Rupert as Mr. Bear fills a teaspoon with the medicine. "It is very strong."

RUPERT'S DADDY TRIES A DOSE

He sips. Now what's he going to do?
He's going to sing. He does—"Cuckoo!"

"Cuckoo! Cuckoo!" He doesn't stop
Until he makes a picture drop.

Although it's foggy Rupert goes
To give the clock cuckoo its dose.

It's lucky Rupert knows the way.
In fog so thick he might well stray.

Mr. Bear raises the teaspoon to his mouth, sips, swallows and smacks his lips. A strange look comes over his face after a moment. Rupert recognises it. It's the look he has when he is about to sing at one of the Nutwood village concerts. He shuts his eyes, takes a deep breath and opens his mouth. "Cuckoo!" he sings—or rather bellows. "Cuckoo! Cuckoo!" He makes such a tremendous noise that a picture is shaken off the wall and crashes to the floor. "My, it is strong!" Rupert gasps.

As soon as the effect of the medicine wears off and Mr. Bear can speak in his normal voice again, Rupert asks if he can take the medicine to Widow Goat's cuckoo clock. "It really did sound rather ill," he coaxes his Mummy who is not very keen about letting him go out in the fog. But when he convinces her that he knows the way too well to get lost she allows him to go. Yet, well as he knows the way, Rupert has to go very slowly from one landmark to the next.

RUPERT CURES THE CLOCK BIRD

They tell him that the Widow comes
By this time every day with crumbs.

Before he looks for Widow Goat
He treats the cuckoo's husky throat.

Now hear that clock bird cry "Cuckoo!
I feel so well now, thanks to you!"

The birds outside look in and cry,
"Let us have some. Oh, do let's try!"

When at last Rupert reaches Widow Goat's home he finds several small rather anxious birds in the porch. "Where's Widow Goat?" they twitter. "Do you know? She's been away for ages. She ought to have been back by now to give us our crumbs." "Perhaps she's got lost in the fog," Rupert says. "Just let me give this medicine to the cuckoo in the clock and then I'll have a look for her." Then he goes inside, climbs onto the chair and gives the cuckoo his dose.

For a moment or two the cuckoo says nothing. Then quite suddenly it gives a loud, clear cry of "Cuckoo! Cuckoo! Cuckoo!" It pauses only long enough to say, "Oh, this is fine! I haven't felt so well for ages!" And off it goes again with its "Cuckoo!" Poor Rupert is wondering how on earth he can get it to stop when he hears a noise at the window and turns to see a crowd of birds. "Can we have some medicine?" they cry. "It seems to have done the cuckoo so much good!"

RUPERT PLAYS A TRICK

"That stuff is not for you, I fear,"
Says Rupert. Then a shape looms near!

It's Widow Goat who says she found
Her way home by the cuckoo's sound.

Says she, "Now you must stay for tea,
And you shall feed the birds for me."

Then Rupert, joking, thinks, "I'll spread
This medicine among the bread."

Rupert hurries out to explain to the birds that the medicine is only for cuckoos. From the porch he sees a shape loom through the fog. It looks quite eerie for a moment before he sees with a sigh of relief that it is Widow Goat. It turns out that she has been lost in the fog. "If I hadn't heard my cuckoo clock and made for the sound goodness knows where I might have ended up," she says. "But why does it sound so loud and clear?" So Rupert tells her what happened.

Widow Goat is so grateful for what Rupert has done for her cuckoo clock that she insists he stays for a meal. Afterwards she hands him a slice of bread and asks him to break it up for the birds who are still waiting for their crumbs. Rupert sees a chance to play a joke on the birds. When Widow Goat's back is turned he pours some of the cuckoo's throat medicine over the crumbs. "It can't do them any harm," he chuckles. "And won't Widow Goat get a surprise!"

RUPERT FINDS A BELL

"Crumbs!" Rupert calls and down they fly.
They eat. They pause. "Cuckoo!" they cry.

Gasps Widow Goat, "What have you done?"
But all the birds join in the fun.

The birds pretend they're cross and chase
The little bear. It's quite a race!

Then suddenly he gets a scare.
A bell falls through the foggy air!

The birds swarm round when Rupert takes the crumbs outside and scatters them. The birds eat them all up and for a moment there is a rather surprised sort of silence. Then "Cuckoo! Cuckoo! Cuckoo!" The noise from the birds is so loud that Widow Goat throws open her window to find out what on earth is going on. At that the birds join in the joke and crowd round her calling "Cuckoo!" until she has to close her window to shut out the din.

Rupert tells the birds that the effects of the medicine will soon wear off and they will sound like their old selves again. They pretend to be angry at this and in fun chase Rupert away from the cottage. After a little Rupert realises that the birds have turned back and that he has lost his way. While he is looking around, something falls very lightly on his head and bounces to the ground. It is a lovely, shiny little bell that weighs hardly anything at all.

RUPERT MEETS THE REINDEER

When Rupert lifts it from the ground
It tinkles with the sweetest sound.

He calls then scrambles up the tree,
But no one's there that he can see.

Horace Hedgehog has heard the bell.
But whose it is he cannot tell.

Then Rupert nearly drops with fright.
A reindeer leaps down into sight!

Rupert picks up the little bell. It tinkles sweetly as he lifts it. "Now where did that come from?" he wonders aloud. "Someone or something must have dropped it from this tree. Hello! Is there anyone up there?" There is no answer. "The tree's the only place I can see it could have come from," thinks Rupert. "I'll climb up and have a look." Being very good at climbing he is soon among the highest branches but there is no sign of anybody. When he reaches the ground again he sees an old friend Horace Hedgehog who has been attracted by the tinkling of the bell. But even Horace who knows most things that go on around the common has no idea whose bell it is. Suddenly there is a swishing noise from above and Horace who is very timid disappears into the fog. Rupert looks up and gets such a shock. For down through the fog bounds a reindeer. "That bell's mine," it says. "It fell off my harness. I heard you ringing it. Thank you so much."

RUPERT AGREES TO HELP SANTA

The reindeer asks, "Please be so kind,
And fix my bell, if you don't mind."

"Now," says the reindeer, "back to work.
But ride with me above this murk."

Then high above the trees they fly
To where a sledge is standing by.

It's Santa Claus, by fog delayed.
"I'm lost," he says, "and need your aid."

"Be a good chap and fix the bell to my harness again," asks the reindeer. Still wondering what all this is about, Rupert obliges. "Thanks," the reindeer says. "Now for being so kind would you like to come with me and meet my master?" And so curious is Rupert that he can't resist the offer. He climbs onto the reindeer's back. "Where is your master?" he asks. "At the top of this tree?" "Not exactly," replies the reindeer. "You'll see." And he bounds into the air.

Up, up goes the reindeer with Rupert clinging to its harness. Up beyond the tops of the trees. Up until they break free of the fog into the evening sunshine above. "There's my master, over there," the reindeer calls. And on top of a cloud a little way off is another reindeer and a sledge, and on the sledge—rather as Rupert was beginning to expect—is Santa Claus. "Can you help me?" are Santa's first words. "I started my rounds early because of this fog. Now I'm lost."

RUPERT'S 'CUCKOOS' GUIDE HIM

Nutwood lies somewhere there below.
But where exactly they don't know.

Poor Santa can't believe his ears.
They can't be cuckoos that he hears!

"Not cuckoos!" Rupert cries in glee.
"Just plain birds who were tricked by me!"

They leave the clear bright sky behind,
And in the fog Nutwood they find.

Of course, Rupert is delighted to help Santa Claus and he scrambles aboard the sledge. "I'm looking for Nutwood," says the old gentleman. "Nutwood?" cries Rupert. "Why, that's where I live." But finding Nutwood is much harder than Rupert thought. The billowing fog beneath them gives no clue to what lies below it. Suddenly Santa cups his ear and cries. "What on earth is that noise down there? If I didn't know that this was England and that it is winter I'd say those were cuckoos." Rupert jumps up in delight. "No, they're not cuckoos and this is Nutwood right under us now," he cries. "Oh, please go down now!" And while Santa eases his sledge through the fog Rupert pours out the story of the cuckoo clock and the throat medicine. "Well, I never! Well, I never!" Santa keeps saying until Rupert breaks in with, "That chimney there. I recognise that. It's the one on my house. Hooray! Hooray! We've reached Nutwood, Santa!"

RUPERT LABELS THE PRESENTS

Says Santa, "I've been so delayed,
I can't stop here long, I'm afraid."

"Here's Bill!" cries Rupert. "And I know
To fetch our chums he'll gladly go."

So Santa empties out his toys,
And Rupert chooses for the boys.

The chums come running up just when
Santa is on his way again.

Guided by Rupert, Santa cruises his sledge over Nutwood having all the houses pointed out to him. At last he says, "Wait. I've an idea. This fog has held me up so much and I've so many other places to visit that I haven't time to go down all the chimneys in Nutwood. Show me where your common is and we'll land there and I shall hand out all the presents there." So down they go and the first person they see is a very startled Bill Badger. "Bill, hurry and fetch all our friends," Rupert pleads. Off Bill darts and while he is gone Rupert helps Santa sort out the toys for he knows exactly what each of his friends wants. With Santa ticking off the various presents on his list, Rupert writes out the labels for them, remembering when he writes "Happy Christmas" to sign it "Santa" and not "Rupert". By the time Bill returns with the others the presents are all ready and Santa is leaving. "You've been a real help, Rupert!" he calls back.

RUPERT GETS HIS REWARD

*The happy chums agree that they
Will keep their gifts till Christmas Day.*

*Bill who's been counting, gives a shout,
"You've gone and left your own self out!"*

*He goes home feeling rather blue
Till Daddy says, "This came for you!"*

*And best of all—he might have known—
A cuckoo clock! His very own!*

Rupert hands out the presents to his assembled pals and makes them promise that since they have had to be delivered early they won't start to play with them until next day. They all promise and it is only when most of them have scampered off home that Bill notices something. "Rupert," he asks, "where's your own present?" "Mine?" Rupert gasps. "My goodness! I forgot to put myself on the present list. Oh, I say, what an awful forgetful ninny I am!"

Although he acts cheerful Rupert really feels terribly disappointed as he walks home with his close pals. But just inside his front door his Daddy is standing, clutching a very big parcel. "Santa called a few minutes ago," he says. "He told me how you'd helped so much you forgot a present for yourself. He left this for you." Excitedly Rupert unwraps it. "Oh, wonderful!" he cries. "Something to remind me of this adventure —a cuckoo clock all of my own!"